LESSON PLANS AND WORKSHEETS

To support PSHE and Citizenship in Schools

YEAR 1

Written and illustrated by Kathryn Goodwin

Published by Shire Educational Limited – September 2003

ISBN 0-9546546-2-5

Introduction

This series of lesson plans, resource sheets and worksheets has been written to provide a complete Scheme of Work for the teaching of PSHE with Citizenship in this year group. When put together with the Schemes of Work for other year groups, it demonstrates progression through the Primary phase.

The scheme is split into thirteen units:

Each unit is designed to last for three weeks and consists of three lesson plans with accompanying resource sheets and worksheets. Each lesson starts with a 'Brainstorm' session, which is intended to provide a lively and thought-provoking start to the lesson. Many of the ideas for this session are suitable for Circle Time. A short teaching input and a suggested activity for the children then follow, with ideas for differentiation for the more and less able. The plenary session at the end of each lesson provides an opportunity to collect together thought and to emphasise the main teaching points.

For some of the units, the suggested activity involves inviting in a visitor to talk to the children. It is worth noting these early on as prior planning will be needed. For Year 1 a visitor is required in Unit 4 Safety For Me.

This Scheme of Work can stand alone, or can be supported by the Partners in Citizenship Home School Diaries as the themes for the units are identical. The home activities supplement the planned lessons, allowing parents to build on the ideas discussed at school and allowing teachers to maximise on the learning experience offered by each theme.

Year 1
Rules – Lesson Plan 1

Objectives
- To begin to recognise the difference between right and wrong
- To begin to understand how rules can help us
- To begin to understand the importance of the school rules

Brainstorm
Introduce the characters 'Susie Star' and 'Gregory Good'. Resource Sheet 1 can be enlarged to show the class what they look like. Tell the class that these two children are always making the teachers happy at school. How do you think they do this? The children could discuss this in pairs, then share their ideas with the whole class.

Input
Look at a copy of the school rules. Some of the rules will hopefully have been mentioned during the 'Brainstorm' session. Read through each rule together and check that the children understand what they mean. Why is it important to have school rules? How do they help us?

Activity
Ask the children to choose one of the school rules and to draw a picture of somebody keeping this rule. They could draw Susie Star or Gregory Good or they could draw themselves. Worksheet 1 can be photocopied to provide a frame.

Provision for less able
These children could select a rule as a group. Additional discussion will be needed about what could be drawn.

Provision for more able
Encourage these children to think about why their rule is important.

Plenary
Share the pictures as a class – can the other children guess which of the rules is being depicted? How many of the school rules can the children remember?

Resources
- Resource Sheet 1 (enlarged)
- Copy of the School Rules
- Worksheet 1 (photocopied)

SCHOOL RULES

Here is a picture of Susie Star and Gregory Good.
They are always making the teachers happy at school.
How do you think they do this?

SCHOOL RULES

Name _____   Date _____

This is one of the school rules:

Now draw a picture of somebody keeping this rule.

SHIRE EDUCATIONAL LTD

BREAKING THE RULES

Objectives
- To begin to recognise the difference between right and wrong
- To understand that our own behaviour affects other people
- To recognise choices which can be made

Brainstorm
Introduce the 'terrible twins' characters 'Billy and Belinda Bad'. Resource Sheet 2 can be enlarged to show the class what they look like. Tell the class that these two children are always making the teachers unhappy at school. How do you think they do this? The children could discuss this in pairs then share their ideas as last week.

Input
Remind the children about the rules that were discussed last week. Discuss how some of the things that Billy and Belinda get up to are because they break the rules.

Activity
Ask the children to look carefully at the pictures on Worksheet 2. Can they identify which pictures show somebody doing something right and which pictures show somebody doing something wrong? They should colour only the 'right' pictures.

Provision for less able
These children could work as a group. Additional discussion will be needed about what is going on in each of the pictures.

Provision for more able
These children could also consider what the children in the 'wrong' pictures should be doing instead. They could draw their own pictures to show this.

Plenary
Share as a class which of the pictures have been coloured and why. If we have done something wrong, how can we make the situation better? Discuss the importance of saying sorry, even though it is hard to do sometimes. Help the children to begin to understand that they always have a choice about how they behave.

Resources
- Resource Sheet 2 (enlarged)
- Worksheet 2 (photocopied)

SHIRE EDUCATIONAL LTD

Here is a picture of Billy and Belinda Bad.
They are always making the teachers unhappy.
How do you think they do this?

BREAKING THE RULES

Name _____   Date _____

See if you can find pictures of somebody doing something right.
Colour them in.

What should the children in the other pictures be doing instead?

SHIRE EDUCATIONAL LTD

Year 1
Rules - Lesson Plan 3

CLASS RULES

Objectives

- To develop a sense of belonging to the class group
- To agree and follow rules for the classroom
- To take responsibility for our own behaviour

Brainstorm

Go around the class getting ideas from the children to finish the following sentence:
"I feel happy at school when……………"

Input

Write the title "Happy Classroom" on the board. Discuss the sorts of things the children might be doing in a 'Happy Classroom'.

Activity

Ask the children to work in pairs to draw a picture of a 'Happy Classroom'. Worksheet 3 can be used as a framework for this. Tell them that you will be asking them to describe their pictures later so they need to be ready to do this.

Provision for less able

Additional discussion may be needed for these children about what could be drawn.

Provision for more able

Encourage (through discussion) thoughts about rules, which would help towards a 'Happy Classroom'.

Plenary

Choose some children to describe their pictures. Why are their classrooms happy? Through discussion and agreement, decide upon up to 6 rules, which the children think would help to keep their classroom a 'happy' place. See if the children can remember all of the rules. After the lesson produce a copy of these rules to go on display in the classroom. The pictures drawn in the lesson could also form a part of this display.

Resources

- Worksheet 3 (photocopied) or paper for paired pictures

Name _____   Date _____

A Happy Class

Draw a picture of a happy classroom.
Think carefully about what makes it happy.
What are the children doing?
Are there any rules which they are following?

SPECIAL THINGS

Objectives
- To think about ourselves and what is special to us
- To begin to see sharing as a positive way to show other people that we care

Brainstorm
Write the word 'SPECIAL' on the board – what does it mean? Bring an object into the class that is very special to you and show it to the children. (This could be a photograph or an ornament etc. It could also be an opportunity to introduce a class mascot.) Tell them you are going to let them share your 'Special Thing' but they must be really careful with it and look after it because it is special. Pass it around the class and ask the children to think about why it might be special to you.

Input
Get ideas from the children for other things, which may be 'special' to somebody. Why might they be special? Encourage them to think creatively – 'Special Things' might be possessions, pets, family members, friends etc.

Activity
Ask the children to think of all the things that are very special to them. Can they fill the box on Worksheet 4 with 'Special Things'? They can draw or write inside the box. Tell them that you will be asking them to explain their choices later on so they need to be ready to do this.

Provision for less able
These children may need some additional discussion time.

Provision for more able
Encourage these children to think beyond simple possessions.

Plenary
Choose some children to describe their boxes, giving reasons for their choices. Discuss sharing our 'Special Things' with other people. It is not always easy to do this. How do you feel when someone shares one of their 'Special Things' with you? Ask the children to bring something special in to school ready for the next lesson.

Resources
- A special object
- Worksheet 4 (photocopied)

Name _____   Date _____

My Special Things

SHARING WITH FRIENDS

Objectives

- To begin to see sharing as a positive way to show other people that we care
- To begin to recognise what is fair and unfair
- To begin to understand how to play and work cooperatively

Brainstorm

The children will need to have their 'Special Things' which they have brought into school for this lesson. Go around the class allowing each of the children to show their 'Special Thing'. (If any children have forgotten, they could be allowed to choose something 'special' from within the classroom.) The children could also say why their object is special to them.

Input

Show the children the pictures on Resource Sheet 3. Which picture shows somebody sharing something fairly? Discuss what the word 'fair' means.

Activity

Ask the children to choose a partner to work with. It would be good to choose a person they don't usually work or play with. (You may want to pair up the children yourself.) Explain that they are going to share their 'Special Things' with their partner in a 'fair' way. This could involve telling their partner all about their 'Special Thing' and allowing their partner to hold it, or it could involve playing a game, depending on the objects.

Provision for less able

These children may need to work in a group with adult supervision.

Provision for more able

Encourage these children to explain how they are sharing in a 'fair' way.

Plenary

Get feedback from the children. How did sharing make them feel? Remind them about any references to sharing in the school or class rules.

Resources

- 'Special Things' (brought in by the children)
- Resource Sheet 3 (enlarged)

SHARING WITH FRIENDS

Look carefully at these two pictures. Which one shows somebody sharing fairly?

SHARING WITH OTHERS

Objectives
- To begin to realise that people have needs
- To begin to see sharing as a positive way to show people that we care
- To take part in discussion about topics of global concern

Brainstorm
Sit the children in a circle. Explain that they are going to play a game in which they have to think about themselves. Call out the words, "Put a smile on your face if ………", and finish the sentence with things we might feel lucky about, eg. "………you had breakfast this morning," or, "……… you got a present when it was your birthday," or, "………you have a friend." The children smile when they think that statement applies to them.

Input
Ask the children to think of other things that put a smile on their face – get some ideas from the class.

Activity
Ask the children to think of all the things which put a smile on their face. They should draw pictures around the smiling face on Worksheet 5 to show these things.
Provision for less able
These children may need to work in a group with adult supervision.
Provision for more able
Encourage these children, through discussion, to explain their pictures.

Plenary
Share some of the children's pictures as a class. Discuss the fact that we are very lucky because we have so many things which put smiles on our faces. There are some children in the world who aren't as lucky as this. They might not have enough food to eat every day or they might not have people to buy them presents on birthdays. Discuss any knowledge the children may have on issues like this – there may be stories that they have read etc. What could we do to share what we have with those children? Discuss the work of various charities the children may have heard of. If the school supports a particular charity, this is an ideal opportunity to discuss it.

Resources
- Worksheet 5 (photocopied)

Name _____   Date _____

I smile because ...

HEALTHY CHOICES

Objectives
- To begin to understand which foods are healthy
- To begin to recognise choices that can be made to improve our health and well-being

Brainstorm
Sit the children in a circle. Explain that we are going to be thinking about food today. Ask them to think what their favourite food is. Go around the circle – each child must tell the rest of the class what their favourite food is. These could be collected together on a flip chart. Repeat the activity but this time describing something they don't like eating.

Input
Write the word HEALTHY on the board and discuss what it means. Look at the pictures on Resource Sheet 4. Which of the foods are healthy and which are not so healthy? Help the children to understand that it is important to eat healthy food and that it is OK to eat unhealthy food sometimes, but not too much! Look back at some of the examples of food discussed in the Brainstorm session – whose favourite food is healthy?

Activity
Divide the children into groups and provide each group with a selection of magazines which contain pictures of food. Ask the children to find as many pictures as they can of healthy food. They need to cut out these pictures and stick them onto a large piece of paper in the form of a collage.

Provision for less able
These children may need some additional discussion time.

Provision for more able
Encourage these children to sort the foods into different groups (vegetables, meat etc)

Plenary
Share each group's collage. Do the rest of the class agree with the examples of healthy food they have chosen? Discuss the need to eat lots of different types of healthy food in order to have a 'balanced diet'.

Resources
- Resource Sheet 4 (enlarged for whole class use)
- Large paper for group collages
- A selection of magazines with pictures of food in them

HEALTHY CHOICES

Look at the pictures of food below. Which of them do you think are healthy?

HEALTHY FOOD

Objectives

- To think about ourselves and the food that we eat
- To know that fruit and vegetables form part of a healthy diet
- To begin to recognise choices that can be made to improve our health and well-being

Brainstorm

Go around the class getting the children to come up with as many different types of fruit and vegetable as they can think of – collect these together on a flip chart / whiteboard. They could have time to discuss with a partner first to generate ideas.

Input

Discuss the importance of eating plenty of fruit and vegetables in order to keep healthy. Introduce the idea of collecting some 'data' about our favourite fruits and vegetables. Tell them that they will be building a 'pictogram' to show the results. Resource Sheet 5 gives the idea of what the pictograms may look like when finished, but for class use you will need to draw out the axes on a much larger scale.

Activity

Ask each child to select a favourite fruit and a favourite vegetable. They must draw a picture of each of these on two separate squares of paper, the correct size for the pictogram.

Provision for less able

These children may need some additional discussion time.

Provision for more able

These children may be able to assist with the collating of the finished pictograms.

Plenary

Work together as a class to collate the pictograms. The pieces of paper can either be stuck in position or just placed ready to stick at a later time. Discuss the results together, asking the children to answer questions such as 'How many people like apples?' Remind the children how important it is to eat fruit and vegetables.

Resources

- Optional use of Resource Sheet 5 (enlarged to show the class)
- Large paper for drawing out axes of pictograms
- Squares of paper on which to draw pictures

HEALTHY FOOD

A Pictogram To Show Favourite Vegetables In Our Class

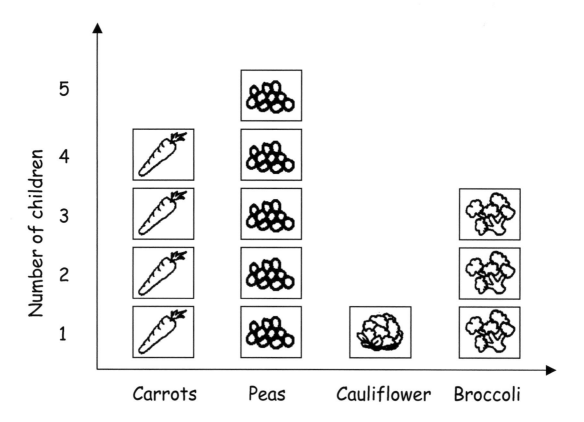

A Pictogram To Show Favourite Fruit In Our Class

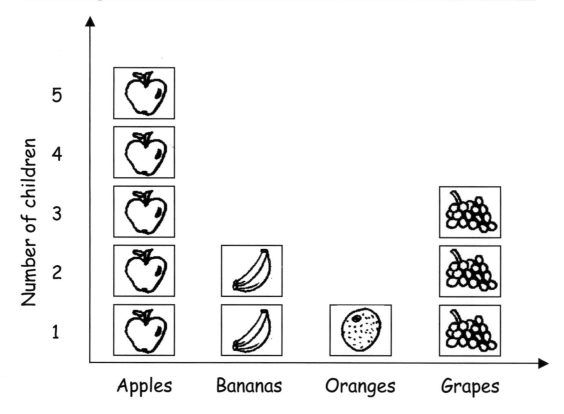

HEALTHY DRINK

Objectives
- To think about ourselves and the drinks that we consume
- To know that milk and water are healthy drinks
- To begin to recognise choices that can be made to improve our health and well-being

Brainstorm
Go around the class getting the children to come up with as many different types of drink as they can think of – collect these together on a flip chart / whiteboard. They could have time to discuss with a partner first to generate ideas.

Input
Look at the list of drinks together. Are any of the drinks healthier than others? Help the children to understand the importance of drinking plenty of milk and water in order to keep healthy. Why is it important? Why are they better than sugary drinks like fizzy pop? Talk about healthy teeth, healthy bones, etc.

Activity
Design a badge that can be worn for drinking milk and water every day. Resource Sheet 6 can be photocopied onto card to provide an outline for this.
Provision for less able
These children may need some additional discussion time.
Provision for more able
These children could be encouraged to think of their own wording for the badge (see design 2 on the resource sheet).

Plenary
Look at some of the badges together and ask the children to explain their designs. Ask them to try to count the number of times they drink a glass of milk or water each day. This could be reported back on in a short class discussion each day over the following week.

Resources
- Resource Sheet 6 (photocopied onto card)

HEALTHY DRINK

<u>Design 1</u>

<u>Design 2</u>

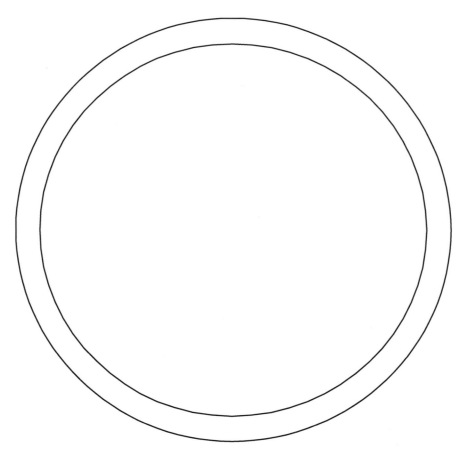

KEEPING SAFE

Objectives

- To think about keeping ourselves safe and to learn from our experiences
- To recognise the difference between right and wrong
- To begin to understand some of the dangers that exist in the home
- To begin to develop rules for and ways of keeping safe

Brainstorm

Write the words BE CAREFUL on the board. The children have probably heard adults saying those words many times! Go around the class inviting the children to describe situations when they need to be careful. They may remember adults telling them or they may remember experiences they have had.

Input

Explain that when they were babies, grown-ups kept them safe all the time. Now they are growing up they have to try to keep themselves safe. They need to learn to think carefully about whether the things they do are safe or not. They need to 'spot dangers'.

Activity

Ask the children to look carefully at the pictures on Worksheet 6. Can they 'spot the danger' that the children are in? They should colour in the object that is causing the danger. They can then try drawing their own pictures where someone is keeping safe.

Provision for less able

These children could work as a group with adult support.

Provision for more able

These children could begin to think about rules for keeping each of the children in the pictures safe.

Plenary

Share work as a class. Can the children put into words any rules for keeping themselves safe? Choose individuals or pairs to come out to the front of the class and (with your guidance) act out a situation when they need to keep themselves safe. The rest of the class must guess what they are doing and remind them to be careful (eg 'Be careful when you use scissors').

Resources

- Worksheet 6 (photocopied)

Name _____   Date _____

See if you can spot the danger in each of these pictures.
Colour in the object that is causing the danger.

Be careful Susie!

Be careful Gregory!

Be careful Belinda!

Be careful Billy!

Now try drawing your own picture where someone is keeping safe

SHIRE EDUCATIONAL LTD

SAFETY IN THE HOME

Objectives

- To begin to understand that all household products, including medicines, can be harmful if not used properly
- To begin to develop rules for and ways of keeping safe

Brainstorm

Explain that today you are going to be thinking about another danger in the home. Discuss the fact that mummies have to watch toddlers to make sure they don't put anything dangerous in their mouths. Lots of things they can find in their homes might look really good but they are actually very dangerous if we drink them. Sit the children in a circle and put a selection of empty bottles / cartons of drink (non-alcoholic!) and household products in the centre. The children take turns to choose a bottle and to decide if it is safe to drink, then explain to the rest of the class how they know.

Input

Make sure the children understand that now they are growing up it is important that they know how to make safe choices.

Activity

Ask the children to choose one bottle / carton which is safe to drink and one which is not safe to drink. They can draw pictures of these into the boxes on Worksheet 7.

Provision for less able

These children may need support in choosing appropriate bottles / cartons.

Provision for more able

These children could also think about designing a label for a cupboard to warn other children about the dangers.

Plenary

Share some of the children's pictures as a class. Pose the question 'What about medicine – is that safe to drink?' Discuss the fact that medicine can help you get better but it can be very bad for you if you have too much.

Resources

- A selection of pictures of or empty bottles / cartons of household products
- A selection of pictures of or empty bottles / cartons of drinks (non-alcoholic!)
- Worksheet 7 (photocopied)

SAFETY IN THE HOME

Name _____   Date _____

Choose a bottle or carton which is safe to drink. Draw a picture of it here.

Safe to drink

Now choose a bottle or carton which is not safe. Draw a picture of it here.

Not safe to drink

OUT AND ABOUT

Objectives
- To know people who can help us to stay safe
- To meet and talk with people
- To know how to ask for help safely

Brainstorm
Invite a visitor who helps to keep children safe (e.g. policeman, lollipop lady) to take part in this lesson. Ask the children if they know what this person does to help the community – brainstorm ideas together.

Input
Ask the visitor to describe his or her job to the children, mentioning in particular ways of helping to keep children safe. It is important that the children understand that they shouldn't go with or ask for help from any adult they don't know, but that there are some adults whose uniforms tell us that they can help us to be safe. The children may also have questions to ask the visitor.

Activity
Ask the children to draw a picture of the visitor on Worksheet 8. This part of the lesson could take place after the visitor has left.

Provision for less able
These children may need some prompting during the discussion part of the lesson.

Provision for more able
Encourage these children to question the visitor about his or her job.

Plenary
Look at some of the pictures together. Are there any other people in the community who help to keep us safe?

Resources
- A visitor!
- Worksheet 8 (photocopied)

OUT AND ABOUT

Name _____   Date _____

A _____ helps to keep me safe when I am out and about.

Draw a picture below.

Year 1
Road Safety – Lesson Plan 1

GREEN CROSS CODE

Objectives
- To begin to form rules for and ways of keeping safe on the roads
- To begin to know the Green Cross Code
- To think about ourselves

Brainstorm
Introduce Harry the Hedgehog to the class. Resource Sheet 7 can be used to show them what he looks like. Alternatively, a soft toy could be used. Tell them that he has been struggling with the problem of how to get across the road safely. Do any of them have any suggestions which might help him?

Input
Explain that there is a set of rules for crossing the road which is called the Green Cross Code. Some of them may have heard of this before. Enlarge Resource Sheet 8 and read it through together, discussing each of the steps in turn, what it means and why it is important.

Activity
The children could work in small groups or pairs for this activity. Ask them to cut out the pictures and captions from Resource Sheet 9 and to try to put them in the right order. They will need another sheet of paper to stick them onto once they are happy with the order.

Provision for less able
These children could work as a group with adult support.

Provision for more able
These children could be given the pictures without the captions – they then need to try to write their own.

Plenary
Go over the order as a whole class. Can any of the children remember all of the instructions without looking at the poster?

Resources
- Resource Sheet 7 (enlarged)
- Resource Sheet 8 (enlarged)
- Resource Sheet 9 (photocopied for groups / pairs)
- Plain paper

This is Harry the Hedgehog.
He has been struggling with the problem of how to
get across the road safely.
Can you help him?

GREEN CROSS CODE

1. **Think** Find a safe place to cross the road.

2. **Stop** Stand on the pavement near the kerb.

3. **Look and listen** Look all around for traffic and listen.

4. **Wait** Wait until it is safe to cross. If traffic is coming, let it pass.

5. **Walk** When the road is clear, walk straight across.

6. **Be aware** Keep looking and listening while you cross.

GREEN CROSS CODE

Look and listen

Look all around for traffic and listen.

Walk

When the road is clear, walk straight across.

Think

Find a safe place to cross the road

Be aware

Keep looking and listening while you cross

Wait

Wait until it is safe to cross. If traffic is coming, let it pass.

Stop

Stand on the pavement near the kerb

SHIRE EDUCATIONAL LTD

CROSSING THE ROAD

Objectives
- To begin to form rules for and ways of keeping safe on the roads
- To think about safe places for crossing the road
- To think about ourselves

Brainstorm
Take the children out onto the playground or into the hall. Make up a pretend road using lines already drawn (or skipping ropes if this is not possible) and talk through the Green Cross Code together, getting different children to demonstrate how they would do each stage on the pretend road. Alternatively you could walk through the whole process as a whole class.

Input
Explain that you are going to be thinking about the first part of the Green Cross Code today – finding a safe place to cross the road. Do any of the children know any safe places to cross the road? Look at the pictures on Resource Sheet 10 (this could be enlarged) and discuss how you would cross the road in each of these places.

Activity
Ask the children to look at each of the pictures on Worksheet 9. Which of them shows a safe place to cross the road? They should colour only the pictures which show a safe place.

Provision for less able
These children could work as a group. Additional discussion will be needed about what can be seen in each of the pictures.

Provision for more able
Encourage these children to explain how why the other places are not safe.

Plenary
Share as a class which of the pictures have been coloured and why. Discuss why the other places are not safe. Return to Resource Sheet 10 – can the children remember how to cross the road safely in each of these places?

Resources
- Resource Sheet 10 (enlarged)
- Worksheet 9 (photocopied)

CROSSING THE ROAD

How would you cross the road in each of these places?

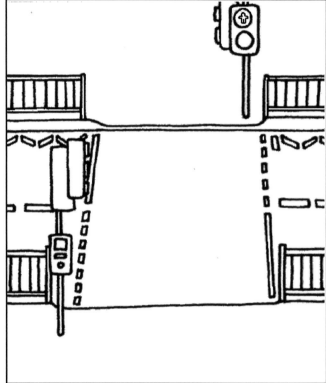

SHIRE EDUCATIONAL LTD

CROSSING THE ROAD

Name _____   Date _____

See if you can find the pictures which show a safe place to cross the road.
Colour them in.

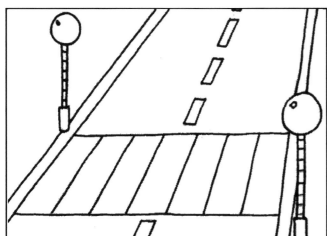

 Can you explain to Harry the Hedgehog how he should cross the road safely at each place?

Year 1
Road Safety – Lesson Plan 3

Objectives
- To begin to form rules for and ways of keeping safe on the roads
- To know how the clothes we wear help to keep us safe on the roads
- To think about ourselves

Brainstorm
Talk through the *Green Cross Code* again as a whole class. (You could use Resource Sheet 8 again for this.) Put actions to each of the stages (eg miming looking and listening) and talk it through with the actions several times so that the children become really familiar with it. Mime one of the actions and see if the children can guess which part of the *Green Cross Code* you are reminding them about. Individual children could also try this.

Input
Can any of the children think what the added danger is when we try to cross the road in the dark? Discuss the fact that wearing bright or light clothing helps the drivers to see you. Show the children an example of some clothing with reflector strips on, and discuss how this is the best way of being seen.

Activity
Ask the children to colour the picture of Susie Star and Gregory Good on Worksheet 10, making them as bright as possible with their choice of colours. They could also draw reflector strips onto the clothing to make them even brighter. (Highlighter pens could be used as fluorescent colours. Poster paints would also provide an alternative.)
Provision for less able
These children may need some additional discussion time.
Provision for more able
Encourage these children to explain their choice of colours.

Plenary
Choose some children to describe their pictures. Which colours have they chosen and why? Discuss the slogan 'Be Safe, Be Seen'.

Resources
- An example of some clothing with reflector strips on
- Worksheet 10 (photocopied)
- Pens, paints etc

SHIRE EDUCATIONAL LTD

BEING SEEN

Name _____   Date _____

Colour the pictures of Susie and Gregory to make them safer when they are crossing the road in the dark.

Be Safe, Be Seen!

SHIRE EDUCATIONAL LTD

CHANGES

Objectives
- To think about ourselves
- To know about the process of growing from young to old and to begin to understand how people's needs change

Brainstorm
You will need to have asked the children to bring in photographs of when they were babies for this lesson. Play a game of looking at a photograph together and guessing who it is. How have they changed?

Input
Discuss the fact that there are lots of things they can do now that couldn't do when they were babies. Think of a few ideas together as a whole class.

Activity
Ask the children to think of 3 or 4 different ideas for things they can do now that they couldn't do when they were a baby. They can record their ideas on Worksheet 11 either in words or in the form of pictures.

Provision for less able
These children could either work as a group with an adult scribe or could think of just one change and record it in the form of a picture on the worksheet.

Provision for more able
Encourage these children to come up with as many ideas as possible and to record them in the form of a list.

Plenary
Choose some children to share their work with the rest of the class. Has anyone thought of any other changes? Introduce the word INDEPENDENT and talk about the fact that because we can do more things when we grow up, we become more independent.

Resources
- Photographs of the children when they were babies (brought from home)
- Worksheet 11 (photocopied)

SHIRE EDUCATIONAL LTD

CHANGES

Name _____   Date _____

What can you do now that you couldn't do when you were a baby?
Draw or write about your ideas below.

Now I'm growing up, I can...

MAKING CHOICES

Objectives
- To understand what is right and wrong
- To begin to recognise choices that we can make
- To take responsibility for our own behaviour

Brainstorm
Play a game of 'Simon Says' as a whole class. (You need to call out various instructions but the children only follow the ones which have "Simon says…", in front of them.)

Input
Discuss how in the activity in the Brainstorm session, the children didn't do everything you told them to do. They only did things when you said, "Simon says". Sometimes other people tell us to do things and part of growing up is to choose for ourselves whether it is right to do it or not. Look together at the situations on Resource Sheet 11. Would it be right or wrong to do what that person is telling you to do?

Activity
Split the class into mixed ability groups of 3 or 4. Ask them to role play together – each child has a turn at telling the rest of the group to do something (they can pretend to be 'naughty' or 'nice') and the rest of the group must decide whether or not they would carry out the instruction. They need to practice saying 'No' if they feel it is the wrong thing to do. (You may want to work through a couple of examples as a whole class to start with.)

Provision for less able
These children will be supported by the others in the group.

Provision for more able
These children will be able to take on more of a lead role in the group.

Plenary
Choose a few groups to act out one of their situations for the rest of the class. Discuss how difficult it is to say no sometimes but you have to follow what you believe to be the sensible thing to do.

Resources
- Resource Sheet 11 (enlarged for whole class use)

MAKING CHOICES

Would you do what these people are telling you to do?

Would you be able to tidy up these coats with me?

Go over to Mary and pull out her chair!

Let's take Surina's pencil. It's really pretty!

Let's ask Fred to play with us today - he looks lonely.

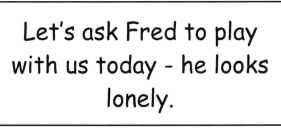

HELPING OTHERS

Objectives
- To think about ourselves
- To take responsibility for our own behaviour
- To begin to understand how we can help people as we are growing up

Brainstorm
Write the words BEING HELPFUL on the board. Ask the children if they remember Susie Star and Gregory Good. (Resource Sheet 1 can be shown again to remind them.) Tell the children that Susie and Gregory are very good at being helpful. What kinds of things do you think they might do? The children could discuss this in pairs then share their ideas with the whole class.

Input
Discuss with the children the fact that now they are growing up, they can help people just like Susie and Gregory. Helping people often makes us feel really good. How could they help at home? How could they help at school? Get some ideas from the children?

Activity
Ask the children to think of a way they can be helpful at home or school and to draw a picture of this on Worksheet 12.
Provision for less able
These children may need some additional discussion time.
Provision for more able
These children could make a list of all the different ways they can be helpful or school instead of drawing the picture.

Plenary
Share the pictures as a class. Can the other children guess what is being depicted? Sometimes being helpful means doing something we don't want to do. It can be hard to say yes when people ask us to help them if we would rather be doing something else. Learning to think about other people and making them happy is part of growing up.

Resources
- Resource Sheet 1 (enlarged)
- Worksheet 12 (photocopied)

HELPING OTHERS

Name _____   Date _____

Now you are growing up you can be helpful.
Think of something you can do and draw a picture of it below.

I am being helpful at _____

BELONGING

Objectives

- To recognise that we all belong to a small community called a family
- To recognise why it is good to belong to a family
- To begin to identify and respect the differences and similarities between people

Brainstorm

Sit the children in a large circle. Explain to the children that you are going to play a game in which they have to think about their families. Call out the words, "Swap places with someone if ………", and finish the sentence with a statement about families, eg. "…… you have a brother," or "……you have an auntie". All the children should be able to swap places at least once by the end of the game.

Input

Explain that we all belong to a family, even though there may be different people in each of our families. Show the children a photograph of some of the people in your family. Why is it good to belong to a family? Get ideas from the children.

Activity

Ask the children to draw their own face in the circle in the centre of Worksheet 13 and then to fill in the faces of some people in their families around the edge. They then need to think of a word that would fill the gap in the sentence at the bottom of the page.

Provision for less able

These children may need some additional discussion time.

Provision for more able

These children could be encouraged to think of as many different words as they can to fill the gap in the sentence.

Plenary

Allow time for children to share their work with a partner. Have they got different people in their families? Collect together and discuss the words chosen by the children to fill the gap in the sentence. Ask the children to bring in a photograph of their family for next lesson.

Resources

- A photograph of some of the people in your family
- Worksheet 13 (photocopied)

Name _____   Date _____

Draw a picture of yourself in the circle in the middle.
Draw some people in your family in the circles around the edge.
Why is it good to belong to a family?

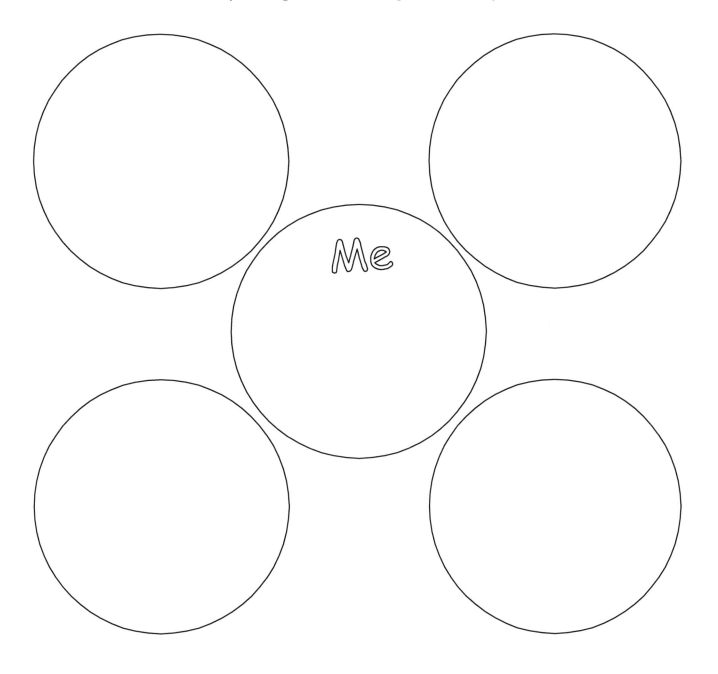

My family help me to feel _____

FAMILY FEELINGS

Objectives
- To begin to recognise, name and deal with our feelings in a positive way
- To begin to see that family members have needs and they have a responsibility to meet them
- To know that families should care for each other

Brainstorm
The children will need to have the photographs of their families which they have brought into school for this lesson. Split the children into small groups. (If some children have not brought a photograph, they will need to be spread evenly between the groups.) Allow time for each child to show the photograph to the rest of the group describe who can be seen. Encourage the other children in the group to ask questions.

Input
Discuss the fact that even though we love the people in our families, we sometimes feel cross with them or fall out with them. Everyone feels cross sometimes. Has anyone ever felt cross with someone in their family? Some children may like to share their experiences. When we fall out with people in our families we still love them.

Activity
Ask the children to try to think of a time when they have felt cross with someone in their family. They can draw a cross face on Worksheet 14 and write a sentence to say why they were cross.

Provision for less able
These children will need support with the writing element of this task.

Provision for more able
Encourage these children through questioning to consider how they ended up feeling happy again when they had been cross with someone.

Plenary
It is not very nice to feel cross with the people in our families for a long time. It is really important to show the people in our families that we love them. How can we do this?

Resources
- Family photographs (brought in by the children)
- Worksheet 14 (photocopied)

FAMILY FEELINGS

Name _____   Date _____

Can you think of a time when you have been cross
with someone in your family?
Draw yourself with a cross face in the box.

Why were you cross?

I felt cross when _____

_____

Objectives

- To begin to identify and respect the similarities and differences between people
- To begin to consider the social issue of money
- To begin to realise that money comes from different sources and can be used for different purposes

Brainstorm

Go around the class asking the children to finish the following sentence: "My family help me to feel……" (This is revision from the lesson at the beginning of this unit.) Collect together all the different words the children come up with on the whiteboard / flip chart. (You could also look back at the list collected in the first lesson – are there any new ones / ones we have forgotten?)

Input

Use Resource Sheet 12 to introduce the Jones family and read the information about them together. Look at the faces of all the people in the family. Do they look happy or sad? Why do you think they are happy?

Activity

Ask the children to read all of the words on Worksheet 15 and to choose the ones which they think will make the family the happiest. They need to copy those words into the family's home.

Provision for less able

These children will need support with the reading element of this task.

Provision for more able

These children could try to put all of their words in a rank order, according to which they think is the most important.

Plenary

Share as a class which words were chosen. The more able may like to say which they put first. Review the idea that some families have a lot of money and some don't have very much but it is not important. What matters is that families care for each other.

Resources

- Resource Sheet 12 (enlarged)
- Worksheet 15 (photocopied)

This is the Jones family. There's Mr Jones, Mrs Jones, and their children Tina, Jack, Peter, Betsy and Lily. They haven't got very much money and they live in a very small house with only two bedrooms. They have to do a lot of sharing! They haven't got a car and they haven't got a television. Do you think they are happy?

FAMILY LIFE

Name _____   Date _____

Which of these words are important to make the family happy?
Copy them into the family's home.

love   money   cars   kindness

understanding   televisions   smiles   hugs

new clothes   caring   computers

Colour the picture to make the family look happy.

DIFFERENT FEELINGS

Objectives
- To begin to recognise, name and deal with our feelings in a positive way
- To think about ourselves and learn from our experiences
- To share our opinions on things that matter to us and begin to explain our views

Brainstorm
Write the word FEELINGS on the board and discuss what it means. Get the children to come up with a few examples of feelings words (eg happy, sad, frightened etc.) Explain that we can often tell how people are feeling by looking at their faces. Look at Resource Sheet 13 together. How do you think the children are feeling? Individual children could then try making their faces show a particular feeling for the rest of the class to guess.

Input
Sometimes things happen which make us feel a particular way. Can the children think of something that has happened that has made them feel happy, sad, angry etc? Discuss a few examples together.

Activity
Split the children into mixed ability groups of 5 or 6 and give each group a set of cards made from Resource Sheet 13. Each group needs to sit in a circle and put the feelings cards face down in the middle of the circle. The children then take it in turns to choose a card, decide what feeling is being shown and to tell the rest of the group about a time when they have felt that way.

Provision for less able
These children could work in a group with adult support.

Provision for more able
These children will need to take on board a leading role in each group.

Plenary
Which of these feelings are good feelings and which ones are bad? Explain that you are going to be thinking a little bit more next lesson about what to do when we are feeling some of the bad feelings.

Resources
- Resource Sheet 13 (enlarged)
- Resource Sheet 13 (photocopied onto card and cut up for each group)

DIFFERENT FEELINGS

FEEELING ANGRY

Objectives

- To begin to recognise, name and deal with our feelings in a positive way
- To think about ourselves and learn from our experiences
- To begin to set simple goals for ourselves

Brainstorm

Go around the class asking the children to finish the following sentence: "I feel angry when ……" It is important that they understand beforehand that this is not an opportunity to 'tell tales' on others in the class. You may want to have a rule that no names are mentioned.

Input

Discuss the fact that feeling angry is not a nice feeling. Sometimes when we are angry we want to hurt people. What can you do to stop yourself getting so angry? Allow time for the children to discuss things that work for them (eg try smiling, count to 10, think a happy thought etc). Focus on the strategy of thinking happy thoughts. Explain that it might help if you had already thought what the happy thoughts were going to be so that you could use them next time you felt yourself getting angry. Get some ideas from the children for what their happy thoughts may be.

Activity

Ask the children to think of as many happy thoughts as they can and to draw pictures to show what they are on Worksheet 16.

Provision for less able

These children may need some additional discussion time.

Provision for more able

Encourage these children to think through for themselves how they will use their happy thoughts next time they feel themselves getting angry.

Plenary

Allow some time for some of the children to show their work. Discuss with the children how they might use their happy thoughts next time they feel themselves getting angry.

Resources

- Worksheet 16 (photocopied)

FEELING ANGRY

Name _____   Date _____

My Happy Thoughts

Year 1
Feelings – Lesson Plan 3

Objectives
- To begin to recognise, name and deal with our feelings in a positive way
- To think about ourselves and learn from our experiences
- To begin to set simple goals for ourselves

Brainstorm
Remind the children that you were thinking about 'happy thoughts' last lesson. Split them into groups of 4 or 5 and ask the children to tell the rest of their group about their happy thoughts.

Input
Explain that yesterday you were talking about using happy thoughts to stop yourself getting angry. Happy thoughts might also help with another feeling – feeling frightened. Everyone feels frightened sometimes, even grown-ups. Sometimes it helps to talk to someone about what frightens you. Share with the children something that makes you feel frightened (eg spiders, thunder etc) then ask the children what frightens them. Does anyone have the same fears? The children should feel reassured by this.

Activity
Ask the children to draw a picture on Worksheet 17 of something that makes them feel frightened. They may like to draw more than one thing.
Provision for less able
These children may need some additional discussion time.
Provision for more able
Encourage these children, through questioning, to think about the different ways in which they can deal with their fears.

Plenary
Choose some children to share their pictures with the rest of the class. Has anyone drawn similar pictures? Do any of the children feel better now they have talked about what frightens them? Discuss the fact that it is also good to feel frightened sometimes because we can stop ourselves getting into dangerous situations.

Resources
- Worksheet 17 (photocopied)

FEELING FRIGHTENED

Name _____   Date _____

I am frightened of...

SPECIAL FRIENDS

Objectives
- To begin to understand the importance of friendship
- To develop relationships through work and play

Brainstorm
Introduce the idea of 'Friends of the Day' – an opportunity for the children to list the things they like about a friend. The class will need to be divided into 3 groups and each group will have their turn at being 'Friends of the Day' during the 3 Brainstorm sessions in this unit. The children in Group 1 take it in turns to come and sit on a special chair. The rest of the class then say why they think that person is a good friend.

Input
Everyone needs to have friends. Some people have lots of friends and some people like to have one best friend. Discuss as a whole class why it is important to have friends.

Activity
Ask the children to think about some of their special friends. They need to draw their faces and write their names on Worksheet 18. Can they say why each of the people they have chosen is a special friend?

Provision for less able
These children may need some additional discussion time.

Provision for more able
These children could also write down why they think each of the people they have chosen is a special friend.

Plenary
Talk about the shape of the circle in the picture – this is a good shape for friendship because there is no start and no end to the circle, so everybody is just as important. Discuss the fact that you could have lots of different sizes of circles – you could have a circle of friends for the whole class.

Resources
- Worksheet 18 (photocopied)

SPECIAL FRIENDS

Name _____   Date _____

Who are your special friends?
Draw their faces and write their names in the circles below.

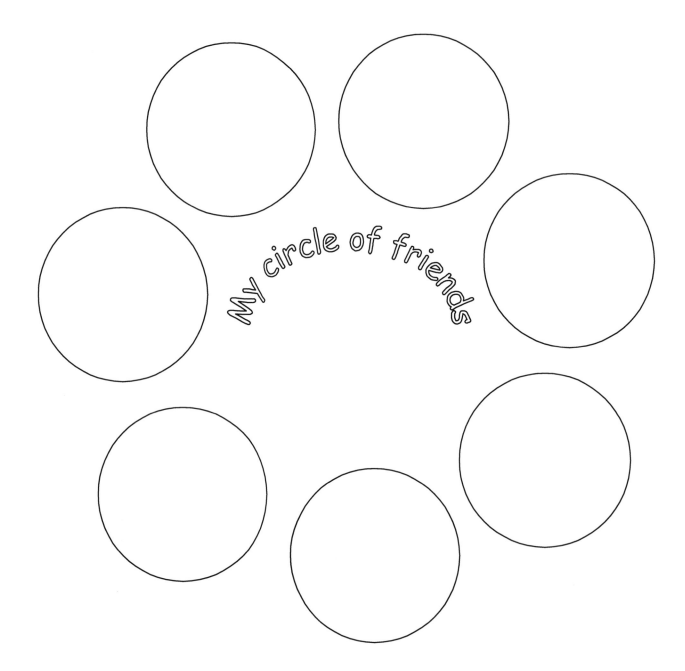

My circle of friends

Why have you chosen these people as your special friends?

Year 1
Friendship – Lesson Plan 2

HELPFUL FRIENDS

Objectives
- To begin to understand the importance of friendship
- To know that friends should care for each other

Brainstorm
Remind the children about 'Friends of the Day' (see last week's lesson plan). This time the children in Group 2 take it in turns to come and sit on the special chair. The rest of the class then say why they think that person is a good friend.

Input
Remind the children what you were talking about last week – why is it important to have friends? We would be lonely if we didn't have any friends. Friends can make us feel special. Friends are there for us when we need them. Can you think of a time when a friend has helped you? Discuss a few examples together.

Activity
Ask the children to think of a time when a friend has helped them. They can then design a certificate to give to that person for being a special friend. Worksheet 19 provides a framework for doing this.

Provision for less able
These children may need adult support for the writing element of this task.

Provision for more able
These children could design their own certificates, instead of using the framework.

Plenary
Choose some of the children to show their certificates and to describe their reasons for choosing that person. Some of them may also like to present their certificates if their chosen friends are in the class. It is wonderful to have friends around when you need them. We must also make sure that we are around for our friends when they need us. Tell the children that you will be thinking a bit more about being a good friend next lesson.

Resources
- Worksheet 19 (photocopied)

HELPFUL FRIENDS

Name _____   Date _____

Design a certificate to give to a special friend.

Special Friend Award

This certificate is presented to ...

_____

for

_____

_____

Signed _____

Date _____

Year 1
Friendship – Lesson Plan 3

Objectives
- To begin to recognise that friends have needs and that we have responsibilities to meet them
- To know that friends should care for each other

Brainstorm
Remind the children about 'Friends of the Day' (see last week's lesson plan). This time the children in Group 3 take it in turns to come and sit on the special chair. The rest of the class then say why they think that person is a good friend.

Input
Ask the children to consider how it has felt when they have been sitting in the special chair and they have been listening to their friends say nice things about them? It has probably made them feel really special. It is nice to feel special and it is really important that we try to make our friends feel special. What could we do to make our friends feel special? Discuss a few ideas together.

Activity
Ask the children to choose one way in which they could make a friend feel special and to draw a picture of it on Worksheet 20.
Provision for less able
These children may need some additional discussion time.
Provision for more able
These children could write a list of all the different ways they can think of.

Plenary
Choose some of the children to share their pictures with the rest of the class and to describe what they have drawn. Sometimes we don't make our friends feel special. We fall out with them. How does that make you feel? Discuss how important it is to try to make friends again when this has happened.

Resources
- Worksheet 20 (photocopied)

BEING A FRIEND

Name _____   Date _____

How can you make a friend feel special?
Draw a picture below.

BEING BULLIED

Objectives
- To begin to understand that there are different types of teasing and bullying
- To know that bullying is wrong
- To recognise how our behaviour affects other people

Brainstorm
Write the word BULLYING on the board. Ask the children if they remember Billy and Belinda Bad. (Resource Sheet 2 can be shown again as a reminder.) Tell them that Billy and Belinda upset a lot of children by bullying them. What kinds of things do you think they do? They could discuss this in pairs then share their ideas with the whole class.

Input
Bullies often try to make us feel sad on purpose and it can be in different ways. It might be by hurting us physically, by saying nasty things or by doing nasty things like hiding belongings. Further discussion on some more examples may be needed. Bullying is a very nasty thing to do. Try to help the children to understand that there is a difference between bullying and the little fall-outs that they often have with their friends.

Activity
Ask the children to draw a picture of a bully upsetting someone on Worksheet 21. They then need to complete a sentence to say what is happening and consider how the person who is being bullied is feeling.
Provision for less able
These children may need additional discussion time and support with the writing.
Provision for more able
Encourage these children to think of as many words as they can to describe the feelings of the person being bullied. They could also think about the feelings of the bully.

Plenary
Choose some children to show their work. Talk again about how nasty bullying is. Tell the children that it is important to tell someone if they are being bullied and that you will be thinking over the next couple of weeks about other things they can do.

Resources
- Resource Sheet 2 (enlarged)
- Worksheet 21 (photocopied)

BEING BULLIED

Name _____   Date _____

Draw a picture of a bully upsetting someone.

This bully is upsetting someone by _____

_____

How is the person in your picture feeling? Draw a face.

BEING A BULLY

Objectives
- To know that bullying is wrong
- To know how to get help to deal with bullying
- To begin to understand some of the reasons why people bully others

Brainstorm
Show the children the picture on Resource Sheet 14. What is happening? Go around the class inviting the children to describe how they think the person being bullied is feeling.

Input
What can you do if you feel you are being bullied? Discuss some ideas together – walk away from the bully, tell a friend, tell a teacher, tell a friendly adult, keep away from the bully etc. Discuss how important it is to tell someone, even if they are scared. Introduce the idea of having a class 'buddy' - someone the rest of the children could talk to if they felt they were being bullied. Children could take on this responsibility on a rota basis.

Activity
Ask the children to design a badge that could be worn when it was their turn to be the 'buddy'. Resource Sheet 15 could be photocopied onto card to provide an outline for this.
Provision for less able
These children may need some additional discussion time.
Provision for more able
These children could be encouraged to think of their own wording for the badge (see design 2 on the resource sheet).

Plenary
Look back at Resource Sheet 14. How do you think the bully is feeling? Why do some people want to bully others? Get some ideas from the children. Perhaps they want to get attention. Perhaps they feel they don't have any friends. Perhaps they wish you would be their friend. Allow some time to discuss the rota for being the 'buddy'. You may like to vote on the best badge to be made up for the 'buddy' to wear.

Resources
- Resource Sheet 14 (enlarged)
- Resource Sheet 15 (photocopied onto card)

BEING A BULLY

What is happening in this picture?

Year 1
Resource Sheet 15

Design 1

Design 2

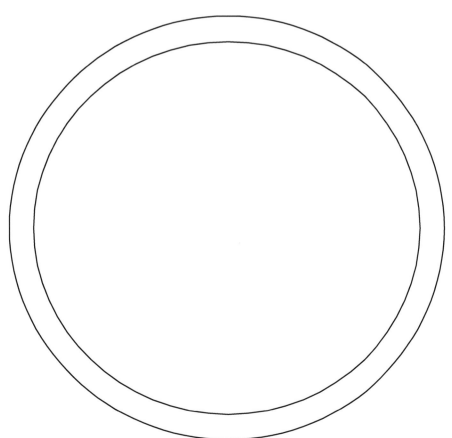

SORTING IT OUT

Objectives
- To know that there are different types of teasing and bullying
- To know that bullying is wrong
- To know how to get help to deal with bullying

Brainstorm
Remind the children that you have been talking about bullying and the different ways we can get help to deal with it. Go around the class getting ideas from the children to finish the following sentence: "If I thought I was being bullied, I would …"

Input
Show Resource Sheet 16. Read through and talk through each of the methods of dealing with bullying with the children. There may be some more to add from the children's responses during the Brainstorm activity.

Activity
This is a role play activity and the class will need to be split into groups of 3 or 4. Explain that you are going to practise some of the ideas for dealing with bullying. Discuss as a class the first scenario on Resource Sheet 17 then allow time for groups to have a go at acting out the situation. Repeat for each of the other scenarios.

Provision for less able
These children may need to work with adult support.

Provision for more able
These children could be encouraged to come up with a scenario of their own.

Plenary
Recap on all of the main ideas from this unit. What is bullying? How does it make us feel? Why do people sometimes bully? What can we do to deal with the problem?

Resources
- Resource Sheet 16 (enlarged)
- Resource Sheet 17 (enlarged)

SHIRE EDUCATIONAL LTD

SORTING IT OUT

Here are some things you can do if you feel you are being bullied. Which ones would you do?

Try asking the bully to play

Tell a friend

Tell a teacher

Keep away from the bully

Tell a friendly adult

Try being nice to the bully

SORTING IT OUT

A bully keeps knocking your pencil out of your hand on purpose when you are writing. You are feeling really fed up about this. Try telling a teacher.

A bully keeps calling you nasty names on the playground when nobody else is listening. You are feeling really upset. Try talking to a friend about it.

A bully keeps spoiling your game on the playground by barging into people and making them fall over. You are really fed up with this. Try being really nice and asking the bully if he wants to play properly with you.

A bully keeps laughing at you because your hair is a different colour. It is making you feel really upset. Try walking away from her then playing with some of your friends.

A bully keeps getting you into trouble with the teacher when you aren't doing anything wrong. It is making you feel miserable. Try talking to a friendly adult about the problem.

SHIRE EDUCATIONAL LTD

TALENTS

Objectives
- To think about ourselves and recognise what we are good at
- To feel positive about ourselves

Brainstorm
Write the word 'TALENT' on the board – what does it mean? Bring into the class a selection of pictures of people the children will know who have a special talent. (They may be television personalities, singers, footballers etc.) Show each person and get the children to describe what his or her talent is.

Input
Explain that everyone has a talent – something they can do really well. Some people are good at lots of things. Get some ideas from the children for things they might be good at.

Activity
Ask the children to draw a picture to show something they are really good at. Some of them may like to draw more than one picture. Worksheet 22 can be used as a framework for this.

Provision for less able
These children may need some additional discussion time.

Provision for more able
Encourage these children to think of more than one talent – they could include things about their personalities.

Plenary
Choose some children to show their work to the rest of the class. Discuss the possibility of some children having received awards / certificates / medals for some of their talents. You could invite them to bring these into school to show to the rest of the class. Some time could be set aside each day for this over the next few weeks.

Resources
- A selection of pictures of people who have a talent
- Worksheet 22 (photocopied)

TALENTS

Name _____   Date _____

What can you do that is really good?
Draw a picture of it in the star below.

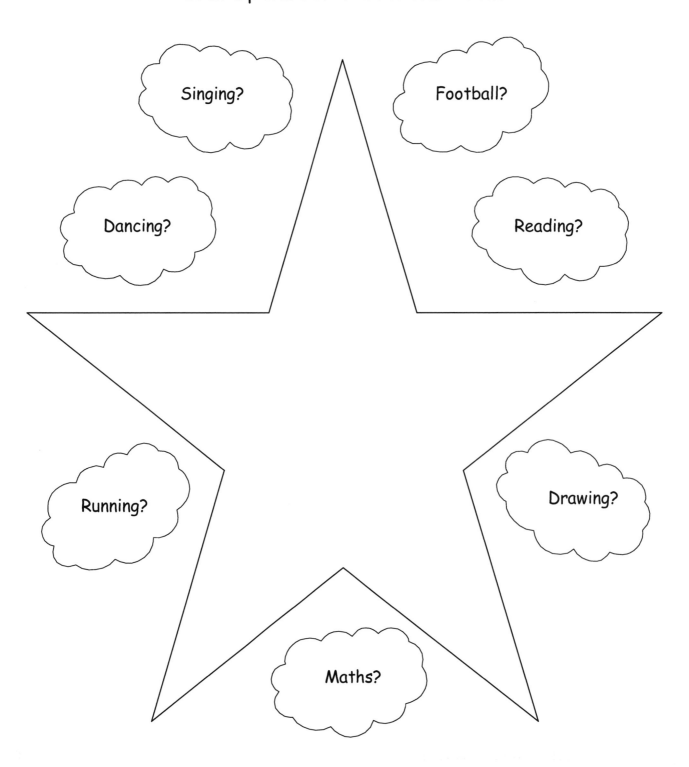

Singing?

Football?

Dancing?

Reading?

Running?

Drawing?

Maths?

Year 1
Feeling Special - Lesson Plan 2

BEING DIFFERENT

Objectives

- To think about ourselves and recognise what we are good at
- To begin to identify and respect the differences and similarities between people
- To feel positive about ourselves

Brainstorm

Sit the children in a large circle. Explain to them that you are going to play a game in which they have to think about themselves. Call out the words, "Swap places with someone if you have ……", and finish the sentence with a personal feature eg blond hair, freckles, blue eyes etc. The children may need to check some of their features with a partner!

Input

Discuss the fact that everyone swapped places at different times. Everyone is different. We are not just different because of the way we look - our personalities are different too. What words would you use to describe your personality? (Kind? Helpful? Talkative?) Get some ideas for more words to describe personalities from the children and make a note of them on the flip chart. (These words will need to be kept for next lesson.) We are all different because we are all special.

Activity

Ask the children to draw pictures of themselves in the middle of Worksheet 23, then to copy some of the personality words from the board around the edge to say why they are special.

Provision for less able

These children will need support with the writing element of this task.

Provision for more able

Encourage these children to think of additional personality words of their own.

Plenary

Choose some children to show their work to the rest of the class. Discuss again the fact that being different makes us all special.

Resources

- Worksheet 23 (photocopied)

BEING DIFFERENT

Name _____   Date _____

Draw a picture of yourself in the box.
Why are you special? Write some words around the edge of your picture.

I'm special because I'm ...

Year 1
Feeling Special – Lesson Plan 3

Objectives
- To begin to identify and respect the similarities and differences between people
- To understand the importance of making other people feel special
- To feel positive about ourselves

Brainstorm
Sit the children in a large circle. Ask them to look at the person on their right and think of something that makes them special. It might be a special talent they have or it might be something special about their personality. Go around the circle getting the children to say what is special about the person they are describing. Repeat the activity, but this time with the children looking at the person on their left.

Input
How did hearing what people had to say make you feel? It is nice to hear people say good things about us – it makes us feel special. Sometimes people are sad because they don't feel special. Telling people that they are special helps them to feel more special.

Activity
Split the children into pairs. Explain that they are going to try to make their partner feel special by writing down all the things that are special about them. It might be special talents they have or it might be special things about their personality. They can use Worksheet 24 as a framework for this. You may want to display the list of personality words gathered last lesson as a prompt for writing.

Provision for less able
These children will need support with the writing element of this task.

Provision for more able
Encourage these children to think of additional personality and talent words of their own.

Plenary
Allow time for partners to show their work to each other. Remind the children how important it is to make other people feel special. Ask them to see if they can make any other people feel special this week.

Resources
- Worksheet 24 (photocopied)
- List of personality words (from last lesson)

THINKING OF OTHERS

Name _____   Date _____

Draw a picture of your partner in the box. Why is your partner special?
Write some words around the edge of your picture.

_____

is special because ...

OUR AMAZING WORLD

Objectives
- To consider what an amazing world we live in
- To share our opinions and begin to explain our views
- To begin to understand that living things have needs and that we have responsibilities to meet them

Brainstorm
Sit the children in a circle. Explain to them that you are going to be thinking about the world that we live in and what an amazing place it is. There are lots of different creatures in our world – how many can we think of? Go around the circle asking the children take turns to come up with as many different names of creatures as they can. You may want to have some pictures of different creatures as prompts.

Input
Discuss together how lucky we are to live in such an amazing place. The world would not be so amazing if it were not for all these wonderful creatures so we have to make sure we look after them. How can we do this? Discuss a few ideas together (eg. putting out food on bird tables, not disturbing bird's nests, putting litter in bins, not treading on insects etc).

Activity
Ask the children to draw some pictures of the biggest, smallest, most colourful and most beautiful creatures they have ever see. They can do this in the boxes on Worksheet 25.
Provision for less able
These children may need some additional discussion time.
Provision for more able
Encourage these children to explain their choices of creature.

Plenary
Choose some children to show their work to the rest of the class. Remind the children again about the importance of doing our best to look after all of these creatures.

Resources
- Pictures of different creatures
- Worksheet 25 (photocopied)

OUR AMAZING WORLD

Name _____   Date _____

What an amazing world we live in.
Think of some of the amazing creatures in our world and draw them below.

What is the biggest creature you have ever seen?	What is the smallest creature you have ever seen?
What is the most colourful creature you have ever seen?	**What is the most beautiful creature you have ever seen?**

OUR ENVIRONMENT

Objectives

- To begin to understand what improves and harms our local, natural and built environments and about some of the ways people look after them
- To take part in a simple debate about topical issues
- To consider simple environmental issues

Brainstorm

Explain to the children that you would like them to think about the school grounds for this activity. Spend a few minutes discussing what there is in the school grounds (trees? grass? play equipment? benches? etc). What do you like about the school grounds? What don't you like about the school grounds? The children could discuss this in pairs, and then share their ideas with the whole class.

Input

The school grounds are part of our amazing world. Sometimes we do things to spoil our amazing world. Discuss how this can happen – get some ideas from the children (eg dropping litter, pollution, graffiti etc). Some of these ideas may have come up in the Brainstorm activity. Focus on the dropping of litter – have you ever dropped any litter on the ground? Why do you think people drop litter everywhere?

Activity

Ask the children to see how many pieces of litter they can find in the picture on Worksheet 26. They can then draw the litter into the bin at the bottom of the sheet.

Provision for less able

These children may need some additional discussion time.

Provision for more able

Encourage these children to think about how else litter can be bad for the environment, as well as making it look untidy and ugly.

Plenary

Allow some time for children to feed back the number of pieces of litter they found. Why is it bad to drop litter? (The able children may have more reasons.) If we all tried hard not to drop any litter, that would make a difference to our environment.

Resources

- Worksheet 26 (photocopied)

OUR ENVIRONMENT

Name _____   Date _____

How many pieces of litter can you find in this picture?
Copy them into the bin at the bottom of the page.

CARING FOR ANIMALS

Objectives

- To realise that pets are living things which have needs, and that we have responsibilities to meet them

Brainstorm

Write the word 'PETS' on the board. Explain that some animals are good to keep as pets, but some animals would not be good. Go around the class getting the children to come up with as many different animals as they can which would be good to keep as pets. You could also allow time for children to talk about the pets that they have got. You could bring in a photograph of a pet you have in order to talk about it.

Input

Discuss the fact that having a pet means that you will have to care for it. You have to make sure you look after a pet properly. What are some of the things you might have to do to care for a pet? Get some ideas from the children and record these on a flipchart / whiteboard.

Activity

Ask the children to draw a picture of one of their pets or a pet they would like to have in the box on Worksheet 27. They must then write down 3 things that they would have to do to take care of that pet.

Provision for less able

These children will need support with the writing element of this task. Alternatively, they could draw pictures to show what they would need to do.

Provision for more able

These children could come up with more than 3 ideas.

Plenary

Choose some of the children to share their work with the rest of the class. Talk about the word RESPONSIBILITY and what it means. Having a pet is a responsibility. You could invite the children to bring in photographs of their pets to show to the rest of the class. Some time could be set aside each day for this over the next couple of weeks.

Resources

- Photograph of a pet (if desired)
- Worksheet 27 (photocopied)

CARING FOR ANIMALS

Name _____   Date _____

Draw a picture of your pet, or a pet you would like to have in the box.

How can you care for this pet?
Write or draw some ideas in the cloud shapes.

SHIRE EDUCATIONAL LTD

HEALTHY CHOICES

Objectives
- To maintain personal hygiene
- To begin to know how some diseases spread and can be controlled
- To think about ourselves

Brainstorm
Ask the children to think about the things they do when they get up in the morning between getting out of bed and coming to school. Explain that you are going to be doing some miming – this is silent acting out of something. Ask for some volunteers to mime something they do when they get up in the morning – the rest of the children must then guess what they are miming. Repeat for several different ideas.

Input
Pick out the ideas from the Brainstorm activity which relate to personal hygiene (eg. brushing teeth, having a wash, brushing hair etc). Discuss why it is important to do these things. Focus on brushing teeth – this is important to keep our teeth healthy. How many times a day should you brush your teeth? Who remembers to do this all the time?

Activity
Explain that you are going to have a challenge to see who can brush their teeth twice every day over the next week. They can record when they do this on a record card. Ask the children to personalise and decorate the 'Brushing My Teeth' record cards on Resource Sheet 18.

Provision for less able
These children may need some additional discussion time.

Provision for more able
These children could include some reasons as to why it is important to clean our teeth.

Plenary
Discuss how the record cards are going to be used – you could send them home to be filled in as part of a homework task. A follow up session will need to be planned to see who has succeeded.

Resources
- Resource Sheet 18 (photocopied onto card)

HEALTHY CHOICES

Brushing My Teeth

This record card belongs to _____

Can you clean your teeth twice every day?

Monday	Tuesday	Wednesday	Thursday	Friday

SHIRE EDUCATIONAL LTD

Objectives

- To think about ourselves and begin to learn from our experiences
- To begin to recognise what we are good at

Brainstorm

Sit the children in a large circle. Explain to them that you would like them to look back over the last year in school. You may want to spend a few minutes discussing some of the things that have happened. Ask the children to think of something that they have really enjoyed about being in Year 1, then go around the circle asking them to finish the following sentence: "In Year 1 I have enjoyed ...."

Input

Discuss the fact that it is nearly the end of the school year and that they will soon be moving into Year 2. They will have a new class and a new teacher. How will this make them feel? Allow time for children to share their thoughts.

Activity

Ask the children to draw a picture of themselves for their new teacher and to write a sentence to tell their new teacher a little bit about themselves. Worksheet 28 has some sentence starters to help the children with this.

Provision for less able

These children may need some help with the writing element of this task.

Provision for more able

These children could write their own letters to their new teacher.

Plenary

Discuss the fact that there might also be some things that they have not been very good at doing in Year 1. Ask the children to think quietly about this for a couple of minutes but not to share what they are thinking with anyone. Talk about a new class being a chance to have a fresh start and to work really hard. It is up to them to make the choice to work hard in school.

Resources

- Worksheet 28 (photocopied)

MOVING ON

Name _____   Date _____

Draw a picture of yourself for your new teacher.

Complete the sentences:

I enjoy _____

I am really good at_____

I am looking forward to Year 2 because _____

_____

SHIRE EDUCATIONAL LTD

Objectives

- To begin to recognise choices we can make
- To think of other people
- To begin to understand what it is to be a good citizen

Brainstorm

Sit the children in a large circle. Discuss with the children how when they grow up, they will have to make a choice about the job they would like to do. Some of them may have an idea already. Go around the circle asking the children to tell the rest of the class what they would like to be when they grow up.

Input

Discuss the fact that we have another choice to make when we are grown up. We can choose to be a good citizen. What sort of things would we need to do to be a good citizen? Get some ideas from the children. Focus on the fact that a good citizen is someone who chooses to help other people.

Activity

Ask the children to think of a way they would like to help other people and be a good citizen when they grow up. They can draw a picture of this on Worksheet 29.

Provision for less able

These children may need some additional discussion time.

Provision for more able

These children could make a list of all the different things they could do instead of drawing a picture.

Plenary

Share the pictures as a class. Can the other children guess what is being depicted? Remind the children about what it means to be a good citizen. Discuss together any people they think are good citizens and why.

Resources

- Worksheet 29 (photocopied)

SHIRE EDUCATIONAL LTD

CITIZENSHIP

Name _____   Date _____

When you grow up will you choose to be a good citizen?
Good citizens choose to help other people.
How will you help other people when you grow up?
Draw a picture below.

SHIRE EDUCATIONAL LTD

Lesson Plans and Worksheets - Year 1. Edition 1, September 2003

PRICE £17.50

Written and Illustrated by Kathryn Goodwin

Published by:

Shire Educational Limited. PO Box 208, Ilkley, LS29 9ZE

ISBN 0954654462-5

9 780954 654627